The CHRISTMAS CAROLING *Songbook*

Melody, Words and Chords
for 72 Favorite Carols and Songs

ISBN 978-1-4950-2801-4

HAL•LEONARD®
CORPORATION

7777 W. BLUEMOUND RD. P.O. BOX 13819 MILWAUKEE, WI 53213

Visit Hal Leonard Online at
www.halleonard.com

ALL THROUGH THE NIGHT

Welsh Folksong

ANGELS WE HAVE HEARD ON HIGH

Traditional French Carol
Translated by JAMES CHADWICK

AS WITH GLADNESS MEN OF OLD

Words by WILLIAM CHATTERTON DIX
Music by CONRAD KOCHER

As with glad - ness men of old Did the guid - ing
As with joy - ful steps they sped To that low - ly
As they of - fered gifts most rare At that man - ger
Ho - ly Je - sus, ev - 'ry day Keep us in the

star be - hold; As with joy they hailed its light,
man - ger bed, There to bend the knee be - fore
rude and bare, So may we with ho - ly joy,
nar - row way; And when earth - ly things are past,

Lead - ing on - ward, beam - ing bright; So, most gra - cious
Him whom heav'n and earth a - dore; So may we with
Pure and free from sin's al - loy, All our cost - liest
Bring our ran - somed souls at last Where they need no

Lord, may we Ev - er - more be led to Thee.
will - ing feet Ev - er seek Thy mer - cy seat.
trea - sures bring, Christ, to Thee, our heav'n - ly King.
star to guide, Where no clouds Thy glo - ry hide.

AULD LANG SYNE

Words by ROBERT BURNS
Traditional Scottish Melody

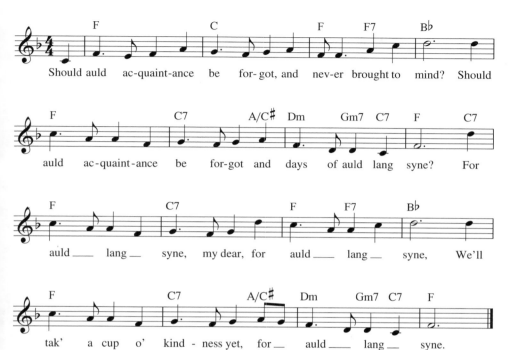

Should auld ac-quaint-ance be for-got, and nev-er brought to mind? Should

auld ac-quaint-ance be for-got and days of auld lang syne? For

auld ____ lang ___ syne, my dear, for auld ____ lang ___ syne, We'll

tak' a cup o' kind - ness yet, for __ auld ____ lang ___ syne.

AWAY IN A MANGER

Words by JOHN T. McFARLAND (v. 3)
Music by JAMES R. MURRAY

A - way in a man - ger, no crib for a bed, The
The cat - tle are low - ing, the Ba - by a - wakes, But
Be near me, Lord Je - sus, I ask Thee to stay Close

lit - tle Lord Je - sus laid down His sweet head. The
lit - tle Lord Je - sus no cry - ing He makes. I
by me for - ev - er, and love me, I pray. Bless

stars in the sky ____ looked down where He lay, The
love Thee, Lord Je - sus, look down from the sky, And
all the dear chil - dren in Thy ten - der care, And

lit - tle Lord Je - sus, a - sleep on the hay.
stay by my cra - dle till morn - ing is nigh.
fit us for heav - en to live with Thee there.

BLUE CHRISTMAS

Words and Music by BILLY HAYES
and JAY JOHNSON

With expression

WHAT CHILD IS THIS?

Words by WILLIAM C. DIX
16th Century English Melody

With expression

1. What Child is this, __ who, laid to rest, __ on
2. *(See additional lyrics)*

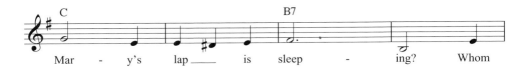

Mar - y's lap __ is sleep - ing? Whom

an - gels greet __ with an - thems sweet __ while

shep - herds watch __ are keep - ing?

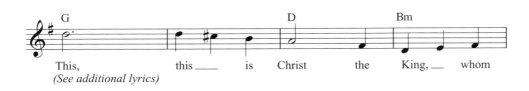

This, this __ is Christ the King, __ whom
(See additional lyrics)

shep - herds guard __ and an - gels sing:

Haste   haste ___ to   bring   him   laud, ___ the

Babe, ___ the   son ___ of   Mar   -   y.

Additional Lyrics

2. So bring Him incense, gold and myrrh,
   Come peasant king to own Him;
   The King of kings salvation brings.
   Let loving hearts enthrone Him,

Chorus Raise, raise the song on high,
   The Virgin sings her lullaby;
   Joy, joy for Christ is born,
   The Babe, the Son of Mary.

CAROLING, CAROLING

Words by WIHLA HUTSON
Music by ALFRED BURT

With a lilt

G | Bm | G | Bm | Am

Car - ol - ing, car - ol - ing, now we go; Christ - mas bells are
Car - ol - ing, car - ol - ing, thru the town; Christ - mas bells are

Gmaj7 | Em | Bm | E6/9 | Bm7 | E6/9

ring - ing! Car - ol - ing, car - ol - ing, thru the snow;
ring - ing! Car - ol - ing, car - ol - ing, up and down;

Em7 | A7 | D | Am

Christ - mas bells are ring - ing! Joy - ous voic - es
Christ - mas bells are ring - ing! Mark ye well the

D | A7 | D | G | D#dim | Em | B7 | Em

sweet and clear, Sing the sad of heart to cheer.
song we sing, Glad - some tid - ings now we bring.

C | G | D7 | G | C6 | D7 | Gsus | G

Ding, dong, ding, dong, Christ - mas bells are ring - ing!
Ding, dong, ding, dong, Christ - mas bells are ring - ing!

CHRIST WAS BORN ON CHRISTMAS DAY

Traditional

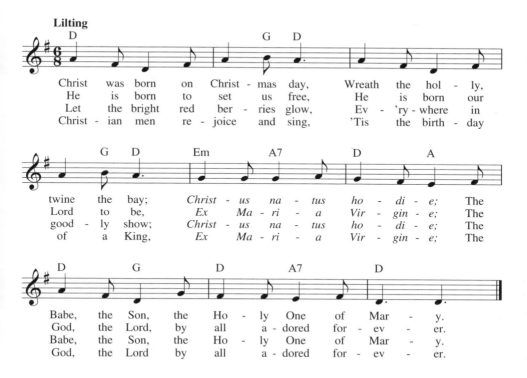

Lilting

Christ	was born	on	Christ - mas day,	Wreath	the hol - ly,
He	is born	to	set us free,	He	is born our
Let	the bright	red	ber - ries glow,	Ev -	'ry - where in
Christ - ian	men	re -	joice and sing,	'Tis	the birth - day

twine the bay;	*Christ - us na - tus*	*ho - di - e;*	The
Lord to be,	*Ex Ma - ri - a*	*Vir - gin - e;*	The
good - ly show;	*Christ - us na - tus*	*ho - di - e;*	The
of a King,	*Ex Ma - ri - a*	*Vir - gin - e;*	The

Babe, the Son,	the Ho - ly One	of Mar -	y.
God, the Lord,	by all a - dored	for - ev -	er.
Babe, the Son,	the Ho - ly One	of Mar -	y.
God, the Lord	by all a - dored	for - ev -	er.

CHRISTMAS IS A-COMIN'

(May God Bless You)

Words and Music by
FRANK LUTHER

Moderately slow

When I'm feel - in' blue, An' when I'm feel - in' low,

Then I start to think a - bout the hap - pi - est man I know; He

does - n't mind the snow An' he does - n't mind the rain, But

all De-cem - ber you will hear him at your win - dow - pane, a -

sing in' a - gain an' a - gain an' a - gain an' a - gain an' a - gain an' a - gain.

Christ - mas is a - com - in' and the geese are get - tin' fat,
Christ - mas is a - com - in' and the lights are on the tree,
Christ - mas is a - com - in' and the egg is in the nog,

Fm7		Eb		F7	Bb7	3

Please to put a pen - ny in a poor man's hat. If you
How a - bout a tur - key leg for poor old me? If you
Please to let me sit a-round your old yule log. If you'd

Eb	Bb7	Eb	Gm	3

have - n't got a pen - ny then a ha' pen-ny - 'll do, If you
have - n't got a tur - key leg a tur - key wing - 'll do, If you
rath-er I did - n't sit a-round to stand a-round - 'll do, If you'd

Fm7	Bb7	Eb	Ab	Eb	Ab	Eb

have - n't got a ha' pen - ny, may God bless you.
have - n't got a tur - key wing, may God bless you.
rath-er I did - n't stand a-round, may God bless you.

Ab	Eb	3	Ab	Eb	3

God bless you, gen - tle - men, God bless you, If you
God bless you, gen - tle - men, God bless you, If you
God bless you, gen - tle - men, God bless you, If you'd

Fm7	Bb7	Eb	Ab	1, 2 Eb	Ab	Eb

have - n't got a ha' pen - ny, may God bless you.
have - n't got a tur - key wing, may God bless you.
rath-er I did - n't stand a-round, may

3
Eb	Ab	Eb	**Very slowly** Fm7	Bb7	Eb	Ab	Eb	Ab	Eb

God bless you, If you have-n't got a thing for me, may God bless you.

THE CHRISTMAS SONG
(Chestnuts Roasting on an Open Fire)
Music and Lyric by MEL TORMÉ
and ROBERT WELLS

Chest-nuts roast-ing on an o - pen fire, Jack Frost nip-ping at your

nose, Yule - tide car - ols be - ing sung by a choir And

folks dressed up like Es - ki - mos, Ev-'ry-bod - y knows a tur-key and some

mis - tle - toe ____ Help to make the sea - son bright.

Ti - ny tots with their eyes all a - glow Will find it hard to sleep to -

night. They know that San - ta's on his way; He's load - ed

Bbm7 · Eb9 · Ab

lots of toys and good-ies on his sleigh, And ev-'ry

Abm7 · Db9 · Gb · Cm7 · F7

moth-er's child _ is gon-na spy ____ To see if rein-deer _ real-ly know how to

Bb9 · Bb7b9 Eb · Bb7 · Eb6 · Fm9/Bb Bb9

fly. And so, I'm of-fer-ing this sim-ple phrase To

Eb6 · Bbm7 Eb9 · Ab Ab7 · G7 · Cm7 · Abm6

kids from one to nine-ty-two. Al-tho' it's been said man-y

Eb · D7 Ab7 · Gm7 Cm7 Fm7 Bb7b9 Eb6

times, man-y ways; "Mer-ry Christ-mas to you."

CHRISTMAS TIME IS HERE

from A CHARLIE BROWN CHRISTMAS

Words by LEE MENDELSON
Music by VINCE GUARALDI

COVENTRY CAROL

Words by ROBERT CROO
Traditional English Melody

1. Lul - lay, thou lit - tle ti - ny Child, By, by, lul -
2. O sis - ters too, how may we do, For to pre -
3.,4. *(See additional lyrics)*

ly, lul - lay. _____ Lul - lay, Thou lit - tle
serve this day. _____ This poor Young - ling for

ti - ny Child, By, by, lul - ly lul - lay. _____
whom we sing, By, by, lul - ly lul - lay. _____

Additional Lyrics

3. Herod, the King
   In his raging,
   Charged he hath this day.
   His men of might,
   In his own sight,
   All young children to slay.

4. That woe is me,
   Poor child for thee!
   And ever morn and day,
   For thy parting
   Neither say nor sing
   By, by, lully, lullay.

DECK THE HALL

Traditional Welsh Carol

Brightly

1. Deck the hall with boughs of hol - ly, Fa la la la la, la
'Tis the sea - son to be jol - ly, Fa la la la la, la
2.,3. *(See additional lyrics)*

la la la. Don we now our gay ap - par - rel,
la la la.

Fa___ la la___ la la la la, Troll the an - cient

Yule - tide car - ol, Fa la la la la, la la la la.

Additional Lyrics

2. See the blazing Yule before us, Fa la la la la, la la la la.
Strike the harp and join the chorus, Fa la la la la, la la la la.
Follow me in merry measure, Fa la la la la la la.
While I tell of Yuletide treasure, Fa la la la la, la la la la.

3. Fast away the old year passes, Fa la la la la, la la la la.
Hail the new, ye lads and lasses, Fa la la la la, la la la la.
Sing we joyous all together, Fa la la la la la la.
Heedless of the wind and weather, Fa la la la la, la la la la.

DING DONG! MERRILY ON HIGH!

French Carol

Moderately

1. Ding dong! Mer - ri - ly on high in heav'n the bells are
2. E'en so here be - low, be - low, let stee - ple bells be
3. *(See additional lyrics)*

ring - ing. Ding dong! Ver - i - ly the sky is
swung - en, And i - o, i - o, i - o, by

riv'n with an - gel sing - ing.)
priest and peo - ple sung - en.)
Glo -

-

-

-

- ri - a, Ho - san - na in ex - cel - sis!

Additional Lyrics

3. Pray you, dutifully prime your matin chime, ye ringers;
   May you beautifully rime your evetime song, ye singers.

DO YOU HEAR WHAT I HEAR

Words and Music by NOEL REGNEY
and GLORIA SHAYNE

Moderately, with feeling

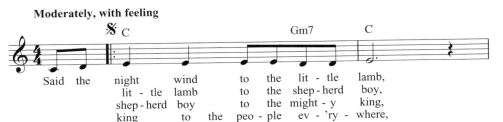

Said the night wind to the lit - tle lamb,
lit - tle lamb to the shep - herd boy,
shep - herd boy to the might - y king,
king to the peo - ple ev - 'ry - where,

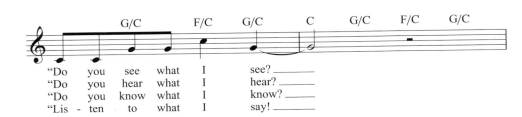

"Do you see what I see? _____
"Do you hear what I hear? _____
"Do you know what I know? _____
"Lis - ten to what I say! _____

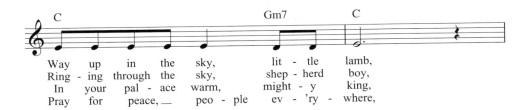

Way up in the sky, lit - tle lamb,
Ring - ing through the sky, shep - herd boy,
In your pal - ace warm, might - y king,
Pray for peace, ___ peo - ple ev - 'ry - where,

do you see what I see? _____ A
do you hear what I hear? _____ A
do you know what I know? _____ A
lis - ten to what I say! _____ The

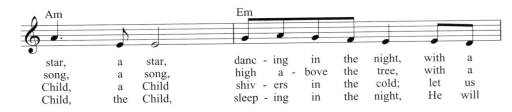

star, a star, danc - ing in the night, with a
song, a song, high a - bove the tree, with a
Child, a Child, shiv - ers in the cold; let us
Child, the Child, sleep - ing in the night, He will

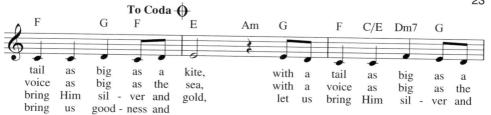

To Coda

| F | G F | E | Am G | F C/E Dm7 G |

tail   as   big   as   a   kite,   with   a   tail   as   big   as   a
voice   as   big   as   the   sea,   with   a   voice   as   big   as   the
bring   Him   sil - ver   and   gold,   let   us   bring   Him   sil - ver   and
bring   us   good - ness   and

| C | Gm7 | 1, 2 C | 3 C | **D.S. al Coda** |

kite."
sea."   Said   the
gold."   Said   the
Said   the

CODA

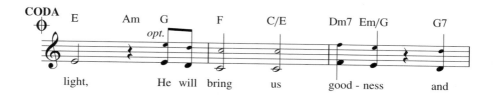

| E | Am G | F | C/E | Dm7 Em/G | G7 |

opt.

light,   He   will   bring   us   good - ness   and

| C | Gm7 C | Gm7 | C |

light." _____

FELIZ NAVIDAD

Music and Lyrics by
JOSÉ FELICIANO

THE FIRST NOEL

17th Century English Carol
Music from W. Sandys' *Christmas Carols*

THE FRIENDLY BEASTS

Traditional English Carol

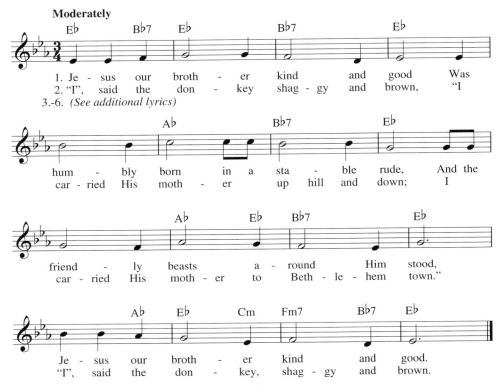

Additional lyrics

3. "I," said the cow all white and red,
   "I gave Him my manger for His bed;
   I gave Him my hay to pillow His head."
   "I," said the cow all white and red.

4. "I," said the sheep with the curly horn,
   "I gave Him my wool for His blanket warm;
   He wore my coat on Christmas morn."
   "I," said the sheep with the curly horn.

5. "I," said the dove from the rafters high,
   "I cooed Him to sleep that He would not cry;
   We cooed Him to sleep, my mate and I."
   "I," said the dove from the rafters high.

6. Thus every beast by some good spell,
   In the stable dark was glad to tell
   Of the gift he gave Emmanuel,
   The gift he gave Emmanuel.

FROM HEAVEN ABOVE TO EARTH I COME

Words by MARTIN LUTHER
Music from *Geistliche Lieder*, 1539

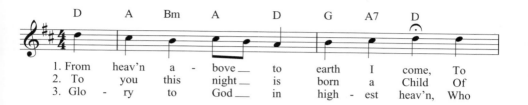

1. From heav'n a - bove __ to earth I come, To
2. To you this night __ is born a Child Of
3. Glo - ry to God __ in high - est heav'n, Who

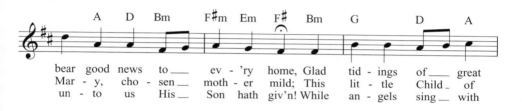

bear good news to __ ev - 'ry home, Glad tid - ings of __ great
Mar - y, cho - sen __ moth - er mild; This lit - tle Child _ of
un - to us His __ Son hath giv'n! While an - gels sing __ with

joy __ I bring, Where - of I now will __ glad - ly sing.
low - ly birth, Shall be the joy of __ all __ the earth.
pi - ous mirth, A glad New Year to __ all __ the earth.

FROSTY THE SNOW MAN

Words and Music by STEVE NELSON
and JACK ROLLINS

found. For when they placed it on his head he be-
cop. And he on-ly paused a mo-ment when ___ he

gan to dance a-round. Oh, Frost - y The
heard him hol-ler, "Stop!" For Frost - y The

Snow Man was a-live as he could be, ___ And the
Snow Man had to hur-ry on his way, ___ But he

chil-dren say he could laugh and play ___ just the same as you and
waved good-bye say-in', "Don't you cry, ___ I'll be back a-gain some-

me.
day." Thump-et-y thump thump, thump-et-y thump thump.

Look at Frost-y go. Thump-et-y thump thump,

thump-et-y thump thump. O-ver the hills of snow.

FUM, FUM, FUM

Traditional Catalonian Carol

Joyfully

On this joy - ful Christ - mas day sing fum, fum, fum.
Thanks to God for hol - i - days sing fum, fum, fum.

On this joy - ful Christ - mas day sing fum, fum,
Thanks to God for hol - i - days, sing fum, fum,

fum. _____ For a bless - ed Babe was born up - on this
fum. _____ Now we all our voic - es raise, and sing a

day at break of morn. _____ In a man - ger poor and
song of grate - ful praise, _____ Cel - e - brate in song and

low - ly lay the Son of God most ho - ly, fum, fum, fum.
sto - ry, all the won-ders of his glo - ry, fum, fum, fum.

GO, TELL IT ON THE MOUNTAIN

African-American Spiritual
Verses by JOHN W. WORK, JR.

GOD REST YE MERRY, GENTLEMEN

19th Century English Carol

GOOD CHRISTIAN MEN, REJOICE

14th Century Latin Text
Translated by JOHN MASON NEALE
14th Century German Melody

Good Chris - tian men, re - joice, _____ With heart and soul and
Good Chris - tian men, re - joice, _____ With heart and soul and
Good Chris - tian men, re - joice, _____ With heart and soul and

voice; _____ Give ye heed to what we say: News! News!
voice; _____ Now ye hear of end - less bliss; Joy! Joy!
voice; _____ Now ye need not fear the grave; Peace! Peace!

Je - sus Christ is born to - day! Ox and ass be -
Je - sus Christ was born for this! He hath ope'd the
Je - sus Christ was born to save! Calls you one and

fore Him bow, And He is in the man - ger now;
heav'n - ly door, And man is bless - ed ev - er - more.
calls you all, To gain His ev - er - last - ing hall.

Christ is born to - day! _____ Christ is born to - day!
Christ was born for this! _____ Christ was born for this!
Christ was born to save! _____ Christ was born to save!

GOOD KING WENCESLAS

Words by JOHN M. NEALE
Music from *Piae Cantiones*

1. Good King Wen - ces - las looked out On the feast of Ste - phen, When the snow lay 'round a - bout, Deep, and crisp, and e - ven; Bright - ly shone the moon that night, Though the frost was cru - el, When a poor man came in sight, Gath-'ring win - ter fu - el.

2. "Hith - er, page, and stand by me, If thou know'st it, tell - ing, Yon - der pea - sant, who is he? Where and what his dwell - ing?" "Sire, he lives a good league hence, Un - der - neath the moun - tain, Right a - gainst the for - est fence, By Saint Ag - nes' foun - tain."

3.-5. *(See additional lyrics)*

Additional Lyrics

3. "Bring me flesh, and bring me wine,
   bring me pine-logs hither;
   Thou and I will see him dine,
   when we bear them thither."
Page and monarch, forth they went,
   forth they went together;
Through the rude wind's wild lament
   and the bitter weather.

4. "Sire, the night is darker now,
   and the wind blows stronger;
Fails me heart, I know not how;
   I can go no longer."
"Mark my footsteps, good my page;
   tread thou in them boldly;
Thou shalt find the winter's rage
   freeze thy blood less coldly."

5. In his master's steps he trod,
   where the snow lay dinted;
Heat was in the very sod
   which the saint had printed.
Therefore, Christian men, be sure,
   wealth or rank possessing,
Ye who now will bless the poor,
   shall yourselves find blessing.

HAPPY HOLIDAY

from the Motion Picture Irving Berlin's HOLIDAY INN
Words and Music by
IRVING BERLIN

HARK! THE HERALD ANGELS SING

Words by CHARLES WESLEY
Altered by GEORGE WHITEFIELD
Music by FELIX MENDELSSOHN-BARTHOLDY
Arranged by William H. Cummings

Moderately

Hark! The her - ald an - gels sing. __ Glo - ry to the
Christ, by high - est heav'n a - dored, __ Christ, the ev - er -
Hail, the heav'n - born Prince of Peace! __ Hail, the Son of

new - born King; Peace on earth, and mer - cy mild. __
last - ing Lord; Late in time be - hold Him come, __
Right - eous - ness! Light and life to all He brings, __

God and sin - ners rec - on - ciled! Joy - ful all ye
Off - spring of the vir - gin's womb. Veil'd in flesh the
Ris'n with heal - ing in His wings. Mild He lays His

na - tions, rise, __ Join the tri - umph of the skies; __
God - head see: __ Hail th'In - car - nate De - i - ty, __
glo - ry by, __ Born that man no more may die, __

With th'an - gel - ic host pro - claim, Christ is __ born in Beth - le - hem.
Pleased as Man with man to dwell, Je - sus __ our Em - man - u - el!
Born to raise the sons of earth, Born to __ give them sec - ond birth.

Hark! The her - ald an - gels sing, Glo - ry __ to the new-born King.

HERE COMES SANTA CLAUS

(Right Down Santa Claus Lane)
Words and Music by GENE AUTRY
and OAKLEY HALDEMAN

HERE WE COME A-WASSAILING

Traditional

Here we come a-was-sail-ing A-mong the leaves so green;

Here we come a wan-d'ring so fair ___ to be seen; Love and

joy come to you, And to you your was-sail

too; And God bless you, and send ___ you a Hap-py New

Year, And God send you a Hap-py New Year. ___

THE HOLLY AND THE IVY

18th Century English Carol

A HOLLY JOLLY CHRISTMAS

Music and Lyrics by
JOHNNY MARKS

Have a hol-ly jol-ly Christ-mas, it's the best time of the year.
hol-ly jol-ly Christ-mas, and when you walk down the street

I don't know if there'll be snow but have a cup of cheer.
Say hel-lo to friends you know and

Have a ev-'ry-one you meet. Oh, ho, the

mis-tle-toe hung where you can see. Some-bod-y

waits for you, kiss her once for me. Have a hol-ly jol-ly

Christ-mas, and in case you did-n't hear, oh, by gol-ly, have a

hol-ly jol-ly Christ-mas this year.

I HEARD THE BELLS ON CHRISTMAS DAY

Words by HENRY WADSWORTH LONGFELLOW
Adapted by JOHNNY MARKS
Music by JOHNNY MARKS

(There's No Place Like)
HOME FOR THE HOLIDAYS
Words and Music by AL STILLMAN
and ROBERT ALLEN

Oh, there's no place like home for the hol - i - days; _____ 'Cause no

mat - ter how far a - way you roam, _____ When you

pine for the sun - shine of a friend - ly gaze, _____ for the

hol - i - days you can't beat home, sweet home. I met a

man who lives in Ten - nes - see and he was head - in' for Penn - syl -

va - nia and some home-made pump - kin pie. From Penn - syl -

I SAW MOMMY KISSING SANTA CLAUS

Words and Music by
TOMMIE CONNOR

I WONDER AS I WANDER

By JOHN JACOB NILES

I'LL BE HOME FOR CHRISTMAS

Words and Music by KIM GANNON
and WALTER KENT

IT CAME UPON THE MIDNIGHT CLEAR

Words by EDMUND HAMILTON SEARS
Music by RICHARD STORRS WILLIS

Moderately

It came up - on the mid - night clear that
an - gels bend - ing near the earth to
world in sol - emn still - ness lay to

glo - ri - ous song of old, From

touch their harps of gold. Peace

on the earth good - will to men from

heav - en's all - gra - cious King. The

hear the an - gels sing.

IT MUST HAVE BEEN THE MISTLETOE
(Our First Christmas)
Words and Music by JUSTIN WILDE
and DOUG KONECKY

IT'S BEGINNING TO LOOK LIKE CHRISTMAS

By MEREDITH WILLSON

hop-a-long boots and a pis-tol that shoots is the wish of Bar-ney and Ben;

Dolls that will talk and will go for a walk is the hope of Jan-ice and Jen;   And

Mom and Dad can hard - ly wait   for school to start   a - gain. It's be -

JINGLE BELL ROCK

Words and Music by JOE BEAL
and JIM BOOTHE

to go glid-in' in a one-horse sleigh. Gid-dy-ap, jin-gle horse,

pick up your feet, jin-gle a-round the clock.

Mix and min-gle in a jin-gl-in' beat, that's the jin-gle-bell

rock. that's the jin-gle-bell, that's the jin-gle-bell rock.

JINGLE BELLS

Words and Music by
J. PIERPONT

JOLLY OLD ST. NICHOLAS

Traditional 19th Century American Carol

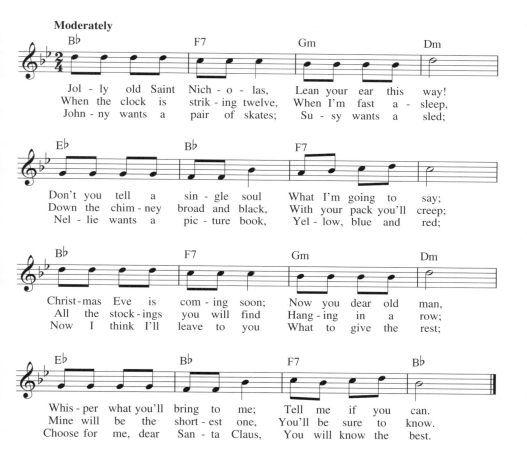

Jol - ly old Saint Nich - o - las, Lean your ear this way!
When the clock is strik - ing twelve, When I'm fast a - sleep,
John - ny wants a pair of skates; Su - sy wants a sled;

Don't you tell a sin - gle soul What I'm going to say;
Down the chim - ney broad and black, With your pack you'll creep;
Nel - lie wants a pic - ture book, Yel - low, blue and red;

Christ - mas Eve is com - ing soon; Now you dear old man,
All the stock - ings you will find Hang - ing in a row;
Now I think I'll leave to you What to give the rest;

Whis - per what you'll bring to me; Tell me if you can.
Mine will be the short - est one, You'll be sure to know.
Choose for me, dear San - ta Claus, You will know the best.

JOY TO THE WORLD

Words by ISAAC WATTS
Music by GEORGE FRIDERIC HANDEL
Arranged by LOWELL MASON

Brightly

Joy to the world! The Lord is come; Let
Joy to the world! The Sav - ior reigns; Let
No more let sin and sor - row grow, Nor
He rules the world with truth and grace, And

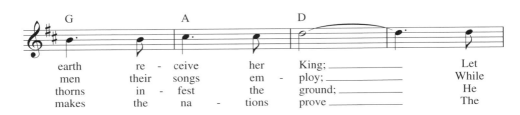

earth re - ceive her King; _____ Let
men their songs em - ploy; _____ While
thorns in - fest the ground; _____ He
makes the na - tions prove _____ The

ev - 'ry _____ heart _____ pre - pare _____ Him _____ room, _____ And
fields _____ and _____ floods, _____ rocks, hills _____ and _____ plains, _____ Re -
comes _____ to _____ make _____ His bless - ings _____ flow, _____ Far
glo - ries _____ of _____ His right - eous - ness, _____ And

heav'n and na - ture _____ sing, And _____ heav'n and na - ture _____ sing, And _____
peat the sound - ing _____ joy, Re - peat the sound - ing _____ joy, Re -
as the curse is _____ found, Far _____ as the curse is _____ found, Far _____
won - ders of His _____ love, And _____ won - ders of His _____ love, And _____

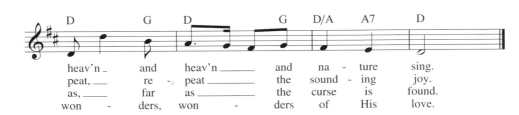

heav'n _____ and heav'n _____ and na - ture sing.
peat, _____ re - peat _____ the sound - ing joy.
as, _____ far as _____ the curse is found.
won - ders, won - ders of His love.

LET IT SNOW! LET IT SNOW! LET IT SNOW!

Words by SAMMY CAHN
Music by JULE STYNE

LITTLE SAINT NICK

Words and Music by BRIAN WILSON
and MIKE LOVE

Run, run, rein - deer. _____ Run, run, rein - deer.

Oh. _____ Run, run, rein - deer. _____

Run, run, rein - deer. He don't miss no one. And

CODA

Lit - tle Saint Nick. (Lit - tle Saint Nick.) Ah, _____

Mer - ry Christ-mas, Saint __ Nick. _____ Ah, _____
(Christ - mas comes this time each year.) _

A MARSHMALLOW WORLD

Words by CARL SIGMAN
Music by PETER DE ROSE

world is your snow - ball just for a song; get out and roll it a -

long. It's a yum - yum - my world made for sweet - hearts; ___ Take a

walk with your fa - vor-ite girl. It's a sug - ar date; _ what if spring is late? _ In

win - ter it's a marsh - mal - low world. _____ It's a world.

MERRY CHRISTMAS, DARLING

Words and Music by RICHARD CARPENTER
and FRANK POOLER

Greet-ing cards have all been sent, the Christ-mas rush is through, but I still have one wish to make, a spe-cial one for you.

Mer-ry Christ-mas, dar-ling. We're a-part that's true; but I can dream and in my dreams, I'm Christ-mas-ing with you. Hol-i-days are joy-ful, there's al-ways some-thing new. But ev-'ry day's a

MISTER SANTA

Words and Music by
PAT BALLARD

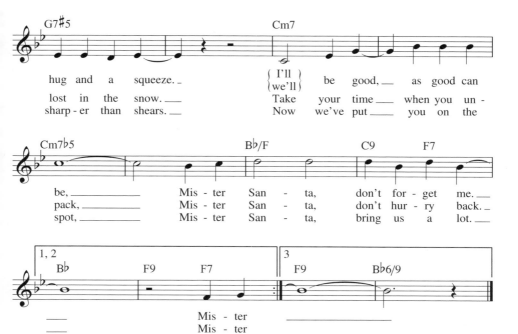

G7#5   Cm7

hug and   a   squeeze. _   (I'll)   be   good, __   as   good can
lost   in   the   snow. ___   (we'll) Take your time __ when you un -
sharp - er than shears. __   Now we've put __ you on   the

Cm7♭5   B♭/F   C9   F7

be, _____   Mis - ter San - ta,   don't for - get   me. __
pack, _____   Mis - ter San - ta,   don't hur - ry   back. __
spot, _____   Mis - ter San - ta,   bring us   a   lot. __

1, 2   3
B♭   F9   F7   F9   B♭6/9

___   Mis - ter _____
___   Mis - ter
                Mis - ter
                Mis - ter

MISTLETOE AND HOLLY

Words and Music by FRANK SINATRA,
DOK STANFORD and HENRY W. SANICOLA

O CHRISTMAS TREE

Traditional German Carol

THE MOST WONDERFUL TIME OF THE YEAR

Words and Music by EDDIE POLA
and GEORGE WYLE

Brightly, in one

It's the most won-der-ful time _____ of the
hap - hap-pi-est sea - son of
most won-der-ful time _____ of the

year, _____ with the kids jin-gle-
all, _____ with those hol-i-day
year. _____ There'll be much mis-tle-

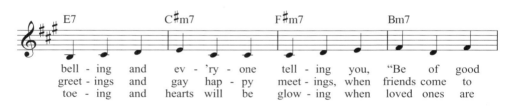

bell - ing and ev-'ry - one tell - ing you, "Be of good
greet - ings and gay hap - py meet - ings, when friends come to
toe - ing and hearts will be glow - ing when loved ones are

To Coda ⊕

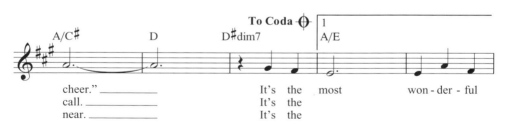

cheer." _____ It's the most won-der-ful
call. _____ It's the
near. _____ It's the

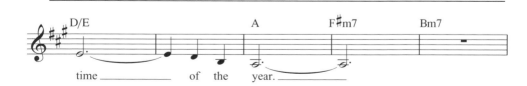

time _____ of the year.

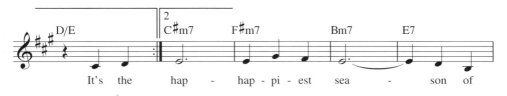

It's the hap - hap - pi - est sea - son of

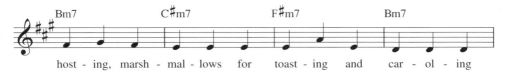

all. _____ There'll be par - ties for

host - ing, marsh - mal - lows for toast - ing and car - ol - ing

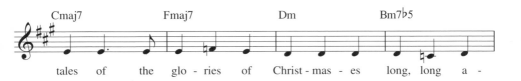

out in the snow. There'll be scar - y ghost sto - ries and

tales of the glo - ries of Christ - mas - es long, long a -

go. _____ It's the most won - der - ful

time _____ of the year. _____

MY FAVORITE THINGS

from THE SOUND OF MUSIC

Lyrics by OSCAR HAMMERSTEIN II
Music by RICHARD RODGERS

things. When the dog bites, When the bee stings,

When I'm feel - ing sad, _____ I sim - ply re -

mem - ber my fa - vor - ite things and then I don't feel

so bad. _____

O COME, ALL YE FAITHFUL

(Adeste Fideles)

Music by JOHN FRANCIS WADE
Latin Words translated by FREDERICK OAKELEY

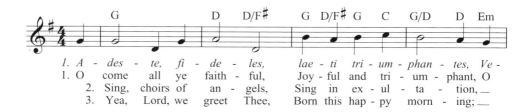

1. A - des - te, fi - de - les, lae - ti tri - um - phan - tes, Ve -
1. O come all ye faith - ful, Joy - ful and tri - um - phant, O
2. Sing, choirs of an - gels, Sing in ex - ul - ta - tion, ___
3. Yea, Lord, we greet Thee, Born this hap - py morn - ing; ___

ni - te, ve - ni - te in Beth - le - hem.
come ye, O come ___ ye to Beth - le - hem;
Sing all ye cit - i - zens of heav'n ___ a - bove.
Je - sus, to Thee ___ be all glo - ry giv'n.

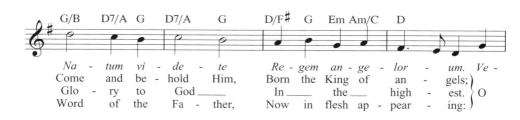

Na - tum vi - de - te Re - gem an - ge - lor - um. Ve -
Come and be - hold Him, Born the King of an - gels;
Glo - ry to God ___ In ___ the ___ high - est. } O
Word of the Fa - ther, Now in flesh ap - pear - ing:

ni - te a - do - re - mus, ve - ni - te a - do - re - mus, ve -
come let us a - dore Him, O come let us a - dore Him, O

ni - te a - do - re - mus ___ Do - mi - num.
come let us a - dore Him, ___ Christ ___ the Lord.

O HOLY NIGHT

French Words by PLACIDE CAPPEAU
English Words by JOHN S. DWIGHT
Music by ADOLPHE ADAM

O LITTLE TOWN OF BETHLEHEM

Words by PHILLIPS BROOKS
Music by LEWIS H. REDNER

O lit - tle town of Beth - le - hem, How still we __ see thee
For Christ is born of Mar - y, And gath - ered all a -
How si - lent - ly, how si - lent - ly The won - drous gift is
O ho - ly Child of Beth - le - hem, De - scend to __ us, we

lie; A - bove thy deep and dream - less sleep The
bove, While mor - tals sleep, the an - gels keep Their
giv'n! So God im - parts to hu - man hearts The
pray; Cast out our sin and en - ter in; Be

si - lent __ stars go by. Yet in thy dark streets
watch of __ won - d'ring love. O morn - ing stars, to -
bless - ings __ of His heav'n. No ear may hear His
born in __ us to - day. We hear the Christ - mas

shin - eth The ev - er - last - ing light; The hopes and fears of
geth - er Pro - claim the ho - ly birth! And prais - es sing to
com - ing, But in this world of sin, Where meek souls will re -
an - gels The great glad tid - ings tell; O come to us, a -

all the years Are met in thee to - night.
God the King, And peace to men on earth.
ceive Him still, The dear Christ en - ters in.
bide with us, Our Lord Em - man - u - el!

SANTA CLAUS IS COMIN' TO TOWN

Words by HAVEN GILLESPIE
Music by J. FRED COOTS

ROCKIN' AROUND THE CHRISTMAS TREE

Music and Lyrics by
JOHNNY MARKS

Rock-in' a-round the Christ-mas tree _ at the Christ-mas par-ty hop, _

Mis-tle-toe hung where you can see _ ev-'ry cou-ple tries to

stop. Rock-in' a-round the Christ-mas tree, _ let the

Christ-mas spir-it ring. _ Lat-er we'll have some

pump-kin pie _ and we'll do some car-ol-ing. You will get a

sen-ti-men-tal feel-ing when you hear voic-es sing-ing,

"Let's be jol-ly. Deck the halls with boughs of hol-ly."

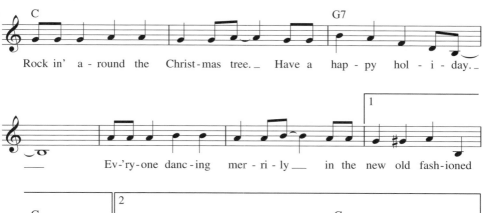

Rock in' a - round the Christ-mas tree. _ Have a hap - py hol - i - day. _

Ev-'ry-one danc -ing mer - ri - ly __ in the new old fash-ioned

way. new old fash - ioned way. _____

RUDOLPH THE RED-NOSED REINDEER

Music and Lyrics by
JOHNNY MARKS

say, "Ru - dolph, with your nose so bright, won't you guide my

sleigh to - night?" _ Then how the rein - deer loved him

as they shout - ed out with glee: "Ru - dolph the red - nosed rein - deer,

you'll go down in his - to - ry!" _____

SHAKE ME I RATTLE

(Squeeze Me I Cry)

Words and Music by HAL HACKADY
and CHARLES NAYLOR

Moderately slow

I was pass - ing by a toy shop on the cor - ner of the
called an - oth - er toy shop on a square so long a -
late and snow was fall - ing as the shop - pers hur - ried

square, where a lit - tle girl was look - ing in the win-dow
go, where I saw a lit - tle dol - ly that I want - ed
by past the girl - ie at the win - dow with her lit - tle head held

there. She was look - ing at a dol - ly in a dress of ros - y
so. I re - mem - bered, I re - mem-bered how I longed to make it
high. They were clos - ing up the toy shop as I hur - ried thru the

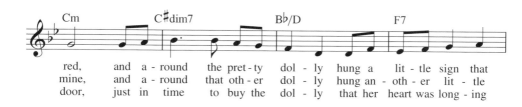

red, and a - round the pret - ty dol - ly hung a lit - tle sign that
mine, and a - round that oth - er dol - ly hung an - oth - er lit - tle
door, just in time to buy the dol - ly that her heart was long - ing

said:)
sign:) Shake me, I rat - tle. Squeeze me, I
for.)

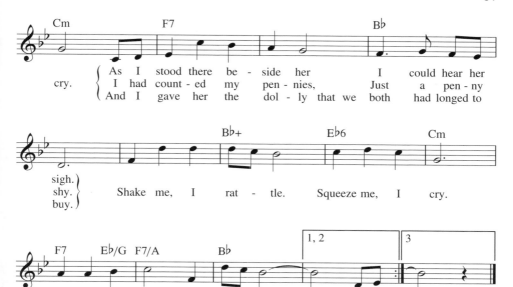

Cm   F7   B♭

cry.
As   I   stood there   be - side   her   I   could hear her
I   had count - ed   my   pen - nies,   Just   a   pen - ny
And I   gave her   the   dol - ly that we   both   had longed to

B♭+   E♭6   Cm

sigh.
shy.   Shake me,   I   rat - tle.   Squeeze me,   I   cry.
buy.

F7   E♭/G F7/A   B♭ | 1, 2 | 3

Please take me   home   and   love   me. _____   I re -
                                                 It was _____

SILENT NIGHT

Words by JOSEPH MOHR
Translated by JOHN F. YOUNG
Music by FRANZ X. GRUBER

SILVER BELLS

from the Paramount Picture THE LEMON DROP KID
Words and Music by JAY LIVINGSTON
and RAY EVANS

SOMEWHERE IN MY MEMORY

from the Twentieth Century Fox Motion Picture HOME ALONE

Words by LESLIE BRICUSSE
Music by JOHN WILLIAMS

THIS CHRISTMAS

Words and Music by DONNY HATHAWAY
and NADINE McKINNOR

TOYLAND

from BABES IN TOYLAND

Words by GLEN MacDONOUGH
Music by VICTOR HERBERT

Slowly

Toy - land! Toy - land! Lit - tle girl and boy - land.
Child - hood's joy - land, mys - tic mer - ry Toy - land!

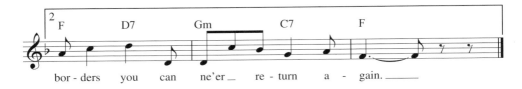

While you dwell with - in it _____ you are ev - er hap - py then.
Once you pass its

bor - ders you can ne'er ___ re - turn a - gain. _____

UP ON THE HOUSETOP

Words and Music by
B.R. HANBY

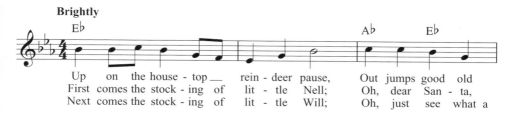

Up on the house - top __ rein - deer pause, Out jumps good old
First comes the stock - ing of lit - tle Nell; Oh, dear San - ta,
Next comes the stock - ing of lit - tle Will; Oh, just see what a

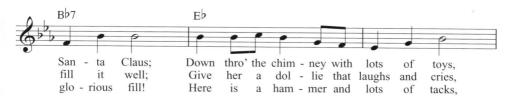

San - ta Claus; Down thro' the chim - ney with lots of toys,
fill it well; Give her a dol - lie that laughs and cries,
glo - rious fill! Here is a ham - mer and lots of tacks,

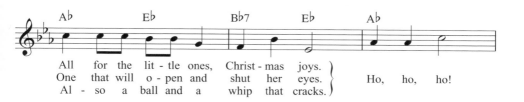

All for the lit - tle ones, Christ - mas joys.
One that will o - pen and shut her eyes.   Ho, ho, ho!
Al - so a ball and a whip that cracks.

who would-n't go! Ho, ho, ho! who would-n't go! __ Up on the house - top,

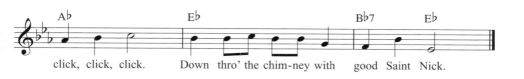

click, click, click. Down thro' the chim-ney with good Saint Nick.

THE TWELVE DAYS OF CHRISTMAS

Traditional English Carol

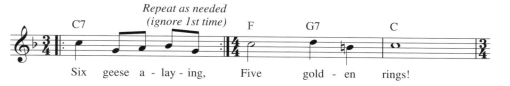

Six geese a - lay - ing, Five gold - en rings!

Four _ call - ing birds, Three French hens, Two _ tur - tle doves, And a

par - tridge _ in a pear tree. On the tree.

7. On the seventh day of Christmas my true love gave to me:
Seven swans a-swimming,…

8. …Eight maids a-milking,…

9. …Nine ladies dancing,…

10. …Ten lords a-leaping,…

11. …'Leven pipers piping,…

12. …Twelve drummers drumming,…

WE THREE KINGS OF ORIENT ARE

Words and Music by
JOHN H. HOPKINS, JR.

WE WISH YOU A MERRY CHRISTMAS

Traditional English Folksong

We wish you a mer-ry Christ-mas, we wish you a mer-ry

Christ-mas, we wish you a mer-ry Christ-mas, And a hap-py New

Year! Good tid-ings to you, wher-ev-er you are; Good

tid-ings for Christ-mas, And a hap-py New Year!

WHAT ARE YOU DOING NEW YEAR'S EVE?

By FRANK LOESSER

May be I'm cra - zy to sup - pose I'd ev - er be the one you chose out of the thou-sand in - vi - ta-tions you'll re - ceive. Ah, but in case I stand one lit - tle chance, _ Here comes the jack - pot ques - tion in ad - vance: _ What are you do - ing new year's, New Year's Eve?

WONDERFUL CHRISTMASTIME

Words and Music by
PAUL McCARTNEY

YOU'RE ALL I WANT FOR CHRISTMAS

Words and Music by GLEN MOORE
and SEGER ELLIS